FAR OUT
FAIRY TALES

INTRODUCING...

PRINCESS KING

PANTS

MRS DAISY SNELLS

HIVES

TATER

MINI

Raintree is an imprint of Capstone Global Library Limited, a company
incorporated in England and Wales having its registered office at 264
Banbury Road, Oxford, OX2 7DY – Registered company number: 6695582

www.raintree.co.uk
myorders@raintree.co.uk

Edited by Abby Huff
Designed by Hilary Wacholz
Lettered by Jaymes Reed
Original illustrations © Capstone Global Library Limited 2020
Originated by Capstone Global Library Ltd
Printed and bound in India

ISBN 978 1 4747 8472 6
23 22 21 20 19
10 9 8 7 6 5 4 3 2 1

British Library Cataloguing in Publication Data
A full catalogue record for this book is available from the British Library.

PRIVATE EYE

PRINCESS

AND THE EMERALD PEA

A GRAPHIC NOVEL

BY MARTIN POWELL

ILLUSTRATED BY FERN CANO

It was a dark and stormy night. Rain was slamming into us harder than dodgeballs in Mr Roland's PE class.

But I didn't focus on that. Because I'm Private Eye Princess King.

And I had a mystery to solve.

I knew this would be a tough case. Snells Manor was a strange place. Everyone said it was haunted.

DOOM DOOMMMM

Of course, if everyone jumped off a bridge . . .

I'm Princess King, from the Royal Detective Agency. Mrs Snells sent a letter asking for help with a case.

And this is my dog, Pants. His clue-sniffing nose will be famous one day.

Indeed. I am Hives, the butler.

Hives stared so hard at me, he must've bruised his eyeballs.

I believe Mrs Snells was expecting someone a bit older.

I doubt a little girl can solve this mystery. So many more, ah, mature detectives have already tried and failed. Miserably.

But I'm only the butler, and that's not my business. May I take your hat and coat, miss?

No, thanks. They're part of the uniform, and I'm on duty. I could use an umbrella, though.

8

9

I am Daisy Snells.

She looked down at us as if she was the queen of the world. With all that jewellery, she certainly looked like one.

What is that *creature* doing here?

That's my partner, Pants.

How unusual . . . Now, this way.

Isn't it rather late for someone so young?

It's never too late for solving mysteries, ma'am. Plus, it's not a school night.

You must forgive walking by lamplight, but —

Yeah, I know.

The storm knocked out your electricity just before I got here.

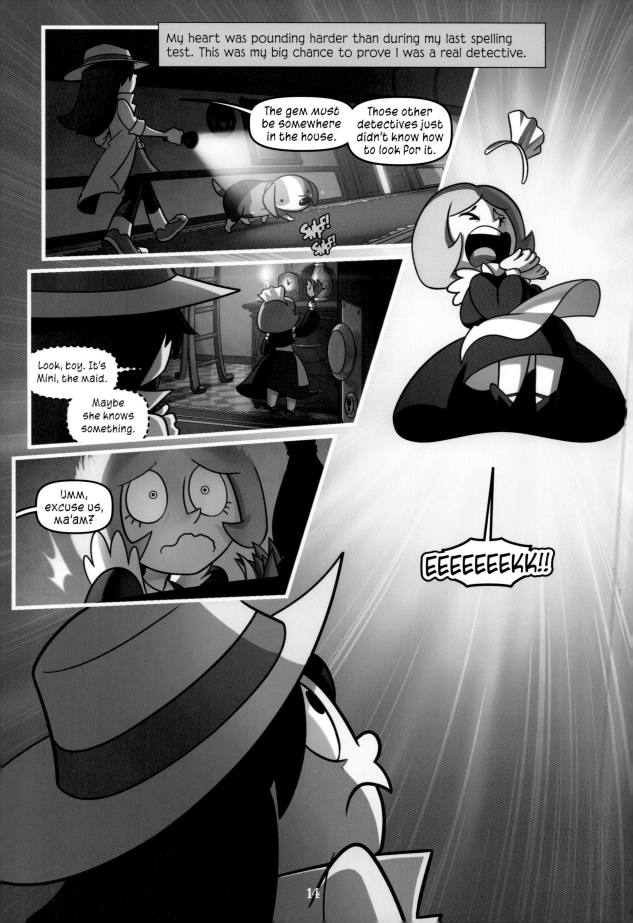

My heart was pounding harder than during my last spelling test. This was my big chance to prove I was a real detective.

The gem must be somewhere in the house.

Those other detectives just didn't know how to look for it.

SNF! SNF!

Look, boy. It's Mini, the maid.

Maybe she knows something.

Umm, excuse us, ma'am?

EEEEEEEEKK!!

16

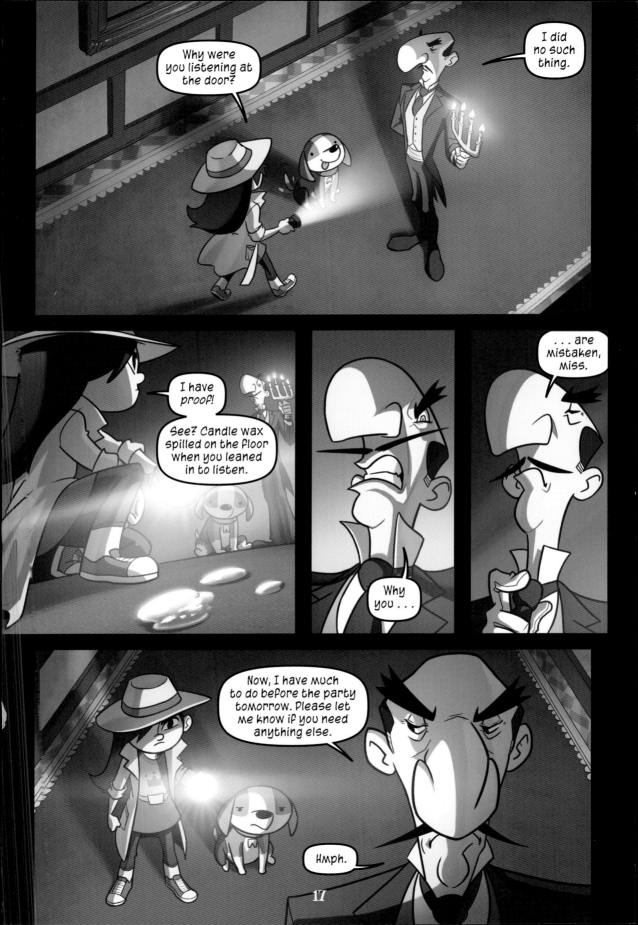

17

Apparently Hives and Mini weren't the only ones keeping secrets – even the manor had a few. But there weren't any footprints on the dusty stairs. The thief couldn't have been down there.

This looks like a dead end, Pants.

Suddenly a noise hit my super-sensitive ears like a booming bass.

If you asked Mini, she'd say it was the footsteps of a g-g-ghost.

WHUMP KA-WHUMP WHUMP

But I don't believe in ghosts. The sound could only mean one thing . . .

Someone is following us!

20

21

You really should stop scaring people!

Listen, Tater . . . I don't get it. What's going on with all the weird furniture?

Oh, that's because Aunt Daisy is really scared of bugs.

She had chairs, sofas and even her bed built high off the floor so creepy-crawlies can't get at her. But she doesn't like to admit her fear to anyone.

SNIFF! SNIFF!

Hmm.

That explained why Mini didn't tell me about the furniture. And Hives must've been listening to make sure she didn't spill the beans. But as soon as I had answered one question, another popped up . . .

You know, Mrs Snells never said you were here. Did she have your room searched?

Nope. I'm her nephew. Why should she?

Tater's room looked like a rubbish dump and smelled like changing rooms. I'll admit, I had my suspicions, but . . .

Yuck, no stolen gem in this mess.

Grrrr . . .

Yay! I'm innocent!

Didn't you already know that?

Yeah, but I was starting to worry that maybe I'd taken it by accident.

"By accident." Hmm . . .

The storm was over and the morning sun was shining. I couldn't wait to throw more light on this mystery.

I don't understand. How did the gem end up between the mattresses of my bed? Who stole it?

I thought it was odd when Mini told me things often go missing. I knew ghosts weren't to blame. So who was moving things?

Seeing you sleepwalking gave me the final clue, Mrs Snells.

Don't you see? No one stole your jewel. You took and hid it yourself — while sleepwalking!

What? Oh my . . .

As I always say: Never rule anyone out. Not even the person who employed you.

You found my jewel. That's the important thing.

You are a true detective, Princess King, and I promise to make sure everyone knows it . . .

. . . as long as you don't start any gossip about me sleepwalking.

Written in 1835 by Danish author Hans Christian Andersen, "The Princess and the Pea" isn't like most fairy tales. It doesn't feature the fantasy elements or magical creatures often found in these stories. But it does have a young woman with unusually strong senses.

The tale starts off with a prince looking for a princess to marry. But he didn't want just any royal lady as his wife. He wanted a real, genuine princess. He searched all over the world but found only fake ones. The prince sadly returned home alone.

One night, during a terrible storm, a loud knocking came upon the palace door. The prince's father, the old king, answered. It was a young woman, completely drenched from the rain. Although she looked nothing like a princess, she said she was of noble blood.

The prince's mother, the old queen, doubted the visitor's claim. So she came up with a test to determine if the woman was telling the truth. The queen crept into the palace's guest bedroom and secretly placed a single pea beneath a stack of twenty soft mattresses. That evening the young woman fell back onto the mattresses, exhausted.

The next morning the queen asked if the woman had slept well. The young woman replied that she had been so uncomfortable that she'd barely closed her eyes all night and even had bruises from the lumpy bed. It was as if she'd been lying upon a rock!

Instantly, the queen, king and prince knew that she must be a true princess — for only a princess could be so sensitive. And so the prince and the princess were married and lived happily ever after.

A FAR OUT GUIDE TO THE TALE'S MYSTERY TWISTS!

Instead of proving she's a true princess, this Princess proves she's a real detective!

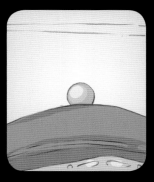 

The green pea has been swapped for a missing emerald jewel.

In the original, the princess has a bad night's sleep. Here, Princess uses her sharp instincts and skills to find the pea.

Princess King doesn't get married in this version. (She's too young anyway!) Instead she impresses a big client and is one step closer to being a world-famous P.I.

VISUAL QUESTIONS

Princess is working the case at night during a storm, and many of the rooms are dark and shadowy. What feeling does this create as you read? How would the story be different if it took place during the day?

1

GRAAACK!

Be a detective! Look closely at the artwork and text, and guess how Mini feels here. What makes you think that?

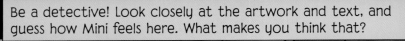

. . . the jewel was stolen by a *ghost!*

2

Things go missing in Snells Manor all the time. It's the work of *ghosts*, I tell you!

What is making the noise in the secret passageway? (Check pages 19 and 20 if you need help.)

3

WHUMP
KA-WHUMP
WHUMP

4

YES!

Most speech bubbles in this story are round, but this one is jagged. Why do you think the shape is different? If you were reading out loud, how would you say this part?

5

In the original fairy tale, the woman proves she's a real princess. How does Princess prove she's a real detective? Look through the story and find at least two examples of Princess using her amazing private eye skills.

AUTHOR

Martin Powell is the author of more than 20 children's books including *The Tall Tale of Paul Bunyan*, which won the national Moonbeam Gold Award for Best Children's Graphic Novel of 2010. Powell is the creator of The Halloween Legion, a nominee for the Stan Lee Excelsior Award, and also an educational writer for Gander Publishing, dedicated to improving literacy reading skills for children of all ages. In 2017, he received the coveted Golden Lion Award from The Burroughs Bibliophiles for his ongoing contributions to the legacy of the adventure and sci-fi novelist Edgar Rice Burroughs.

ILLUSTRATOR

Fern Cano is an illustrator born in Mexico City, Mexico. He currently lives in Monterrey, Mexico, where he makes a living as an illustrator and colourist. He has done work for Marvel, DC Comics and role-playing games such as Pathfinder from Paizo Publishing. In his spare time, he enjoys spending time with friends, singing, rowing and drawing!

GLOSSARY

admit agree something is true, but often not wanting to say so

case set of events that needs to be studied and checked by the police (or a private investigator!)

examine check very carefully

lookout watch carefully for something that is expected or feared

manor main house on a large piece of land; usually a manor is a very big, expensive house

possibility something that might happen or be true

private investigator (P.I.) person who is not a member of the police force but can be employed to gather information or look into possible crimes; also called a private eye

proof something that shows something else to be true

sensitive quickly able to notice or feel small changes around you

solve find the answer to a problem or mystery

valuable worth a lot of money

wick string-like part of a candle or lamp that is lit

AWESOMELY EVER AFTER.

FAR OUT FAIRY TALES